CONTENTS

Oi! Get Off Our Train
by John Burningham

READ & RESPOND

Oi! Get Off Our Train

CREDITS

Published by Scholastic Ltd,
Villiers House,
Clarendon Avenue,
Leamington Spa,
Warwickshire CV32 5PR
Text © Elaine Sturman and Jo Melhuish
© 1997 Scholastic Ltd
  3 4 5 6 7 8 9 0   8 9 0 1 2 3 4 5 6

Authors Elaine Sturman and Jo Melhuish
Editor Jane Bishop
Series designer Lynne Joesbury
Designer Claire Belcher
Illustrations redrawn by Claire Belcher from originals by John Burningham
Cover illustration John Burningham

Designed using Aldus Pagemaker

British Library Cataloguing-in-Publication Data
A catalogue record for this book is available from the British Library.

ISBN 0-590-53730-X

ACKNOWLEDGEMENTS

Mike Goldwater/Network for the use of a photograph of a rubber tapper © Mike Goldwater.
Thanks to **Oxfam** for their assistance in providing material.
Random House Children's Books for the photograph of John Burningham and the use of text, front cover and adapted illustrations from *Oi! Get Off Our Train* by John Burningham © 1989, John Burningham (1989, Jonathan Cape Ltd).

INTRODUCTION

Oi! Get Off Our Train
by John Burningham

WHAT'S SO GOOD ABOUT THIS BOOK?

Oi! Get Off Our Train is a picture book. But that doesn't mean it is babyish. The pictures are exciting, full of colours, techniques and details which make you want to go on looking at them. Perhaps you could even have a go at creating the same effects yourself.

There aren't many words in this book. But that doesn't mean there isn't much of a story. The book makes you think about how stories work. And it has an important message.

ABOUT JOHN BURNINGHAM

John Burningham wrote and illustrated his first book *Borka* in 1963. He started off as an illustrator but nobody would give him a book to illustrate, so he decided to write his own. That very first book won a medal.

For over thirty years John Burningham has been writing and illustrating books for children. He publishes a new title nearly every year. You may remember reading some of them such as *Mr Gumpy's Outing* or *The Shopping Basket*.

John Burningham is married to Helen Oxenbury. She too is an illustrator of children's books. You might know *We're going on a bear hunt*. They have two daughters and one son and they live in London.

What can we find out from the cover?

● Look carefully at the front cover of the book. What do you think might be in this story?

● Write your ideas here.
I think this story ...

_____

_____

_____

_____

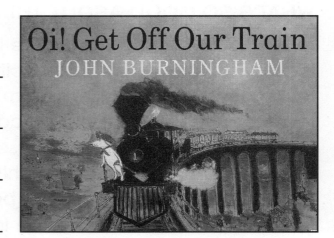

● Now think about the title of the book and answer these questions.

Whose train is it? Write your ideas here:

_____

_____

Who or what might be told to get off the train?

Write it here: _____

_____

Why? _____

_____

John Burningham is the author of this book and he also drew the pictures. He is the author and the illustrator.

● Look at the cover picture for a few minutes. It might give you some ideas about the story.

What sort of train is it?

_____

Where is it going?

_____

Who is on the train?

_____

What do you think this book is about? There are lots of possible answers. Here are a few suggestions which other children have made.

- travelling around the world
- saving animals
- the weather
- a dream

● Write what you think it is about.

I think this book is about _____

_____

Is it a boy or a girl?

Is the child in the story a boy or a girl?
● Tick the box you agree with:

☐ I think it is a boy

☐ I think it is a girl

☐ I am not sure if it is a boy or a girl

When other children were asked the question they said:

1   I think it's a boy because boys play with trains.

2   It looks like a boy's haircut.

3   Girls would have pyjamas like that.

4   Girls can play with trains too.

5   Some girls have their hair like that.

6   Only boys can drive trains.

7   It's an engine-driver's cap, so a girl could wear it if she was an engine-driver.

8   The cap looks like a boy's cap.

9   There is no name in the book.

10 There are no words in the book that tell you whether it is a girl or a boy (for example he/his for a boy, she/her for a girl).

● Decide where each sentence goes in this chart. Write the numbers in the column where you think they fit best.

● Look carefully at the book to help you decide.

AGREE	DISAGREE	NOT SURE

Now that you have thought about all the sentences, do you think the story is about a boy or a girl? Or do you think it doesn't matter?

_____

Have you changed your mind or not? Why?

_____

Does John Burningham know if the story is about a boy or a girl? Put a circle around one: Yes / No

Why didn't he give us any clues?

_____

The elephant

● Read up to where the elephant asks to get on the train. When the elephant wants to get on the train, what are the train driver and the dog thinking?

● Write their thoughts in the bubbles.

Oi! Get off our train

Then the elephant speaks. What do they think now?
● Write their thoughts in the bubbles.

Please let me come

The train driver and the dog have changed their minds.
They let the elephant get on the train.

How do you know that they have changed their minds?
● Write your ideas here:

_____

_____

_____

Why do you think they changed their minds?
● Write it here:

_____

_____

_____

The crane

● Read up to where the crane wants to get on the train. The story up to now has followed a similar pattern.

● Fill in the gaps in the chart below for the animals who are already on the train. Use the book if you need to.

animal	reaction	request	reason	weather
elephant		please let me come with you on your train		hot day
	oi! get off our train		people are making the water very dirty	

Now the crane wants to get on the train.

What do you think the reaction will be?

_____

What do you think the crane's request will be?

_____

What do you think the crane's reason might be?

_____

What do you think the weather might be?

_____

What animal might get on the train next?

_____

● Read on to see if you guessed right!

● Add more information about other animals to the chart as you continue to read the book.

... and soon there will be none of us left

● Read up to where the polar bear gets on the train.
All the animals want to get on the train because they are
in danger.

● Look at these statements and draw a line from each animal
to the reason it is in danger.

Take care! Some animals have more than one reason.

They are cutting down the forests where I live.

I can't live on dry land.

They are catching too many fish.

People are making the water very dirty.

They are draining the water from the marshes.

Someone is coming to cut off my tusks.

Somebody wants my fur to make a coat out of.

I won't have enough to eat.

Some of the animals are in danger because they are being hunted.

● Write these animals here:

```
┌─────────────────┐   ┌─────────────────┐
│                 │   │                 │
│                 │   │                 │
│                 │   │                 │
└─────────────────┘   └─────────────────┘
```

Some of the animals are in danger because the places where they live are being spoiled.

● Write these animals here:

```
┌───────────┐   ┌───────────┐   ┌───────────┐
│           │   │           │   │           │
│           │   │           │   │           │
└───────────┘   └───────────┘   └───────────┘
```

● Write about what is happening to the animals. One has been done for you.

Some people hunt elephants so that they can cut off their tusks.

_____

_____

_____

_____

_____

_____

Was it all a dream?

● Read to the end of the book.
Do you think the child was dreaming the story, or did it really happen?

Here are some clues from the pictures in the book.
● Read each sentence and think carefully.

1   The train is a toy.
2   There is an elephant in the hall.
3   There is a seal in the bath.
4   The child is in bed asleep.
5   In the morning the child is still in bed.
6   There is a crane in the washing.
7   The mother says, 'Is it anything to do with you?'
8   There is a tiger on the stairs.
9   The train looks just the same at the beginning and at the end.
10   There is a polar bear by the fridge.

● Decide where each sentence goes in the chart, and write the number in the column where you think it fits best.

It was a dream.	It really happened.

Have you decided whether the story was a dream or not?
● Choose one of these pieces of writing to finish.

I think it is a dream because _____

_____

_____

_____

_____

_____

I think it really happened because _____

_____

_____

Or you may have a different idea. If you do, write it here.

_____

_____

_____

The weather

There are five double pages about five different kinds of weather in the book. They are:

strong wind   foggy   rain   very hot   snow

● Write the different kinds of weather in the same order as they come in the story.

1 _____   4 _____

2 _____   5 _____

3 _____

The passengers on the train enjoy themselves in all the different kinds of weather. They:

- fly kites
- throw snowballs
- play ghosts
- muck about with umbrellas
- go for a swim

● Match what the passengers do with the weather words in the order they appear in the story.

	weather	what the passengers do
1	_____	_____
2	_____	_____
3	_____	_____
4	_____	_____
5	_____	_____

● Now find the weather pages in the book and check the order.

● Look carefully at the pictures.
Who do you think might be saying these words?

> I wish I could squirt water like that.

> I don't need an umbrella. I don't mind getting wet.

Name _____

Name _____

Weather _____

Weather _____

> Look out! There's a huge snowball behind you.

> This is a bit scary.

Name _____

Name _____

Weather _____

Weather _____

The pyjama-case dog's train journey

The pyjama-case dog has an important part to play on the train journey. After it was over, he wrote about it. Here are some of the things the dog wrote.

● Finish the story by writing in the spaces.

We went on a fabulous train journey. To keep the engine going

I had to _____

An elephant wanted to come on the train. At first we _____

_____

But when the elephant told us _____

Lots of other endangered animals wanted to come on the train.

The tiger told us _____

We had all kinds of different weather. It was _____

_____

I liked swimming best. The elephant _____

_____

There was a lot of snow. We were getting stuck. The animals

_____

The next morning, I _____

Too many animals

● Turn to the page where the polar bear speaks.

● Imagine that the tiger decides that it does not want the polar bear to come on the train. But the crane disagrees – it thinks the polar bear should be allowed to get on.

> There are already too many animals on our train. We can't save everybody!

> I think we should look after all the animals.
> I can understand how the polar bear feels.

● On a separate sheet draw pictures of the two animals. Draw speech bubbles and fill in what they say to each other.

What do the other passengers say?

Do you think the polar bear should be allowed to join the train, or not? Why?

Endangered species

Animals in danger are called endangered species. But the animals in *Oi! Get Off Our Train* are not the only animals in danger.

● Use information books to find out about another endangered animal.

● Write what you find out here.

Another endangered animal is _____ .

It lives in _____

It looks like this:

It is in danger because _____

_____

_____

_____

● Now imagine that your endangered animal wants to join the train. Use the information you have found out to draft two new pages for the book.

● Use two pages from the book as an example, but add your own pictures and words.

Oi! get off our train

Please let me come _____

Who was Chico Mendes?

● Look at the fourth page of the book, just before the story begins. You will see these words:

For Chico Mendes
who tried so hard to protect the rainforest of Brazil.

This is called the dedication. Writers usually dedicate their books to someone who is special to them.

WHO WAS CHICO MENDES?

● Read this information about him. Chico Mendes was born and brought up in the rainforest of Brazil. When Chico was nine years old he started going to work with his father and learned how to collect rubber from trees.

As Chico grew up, he worried about what was happening to the rainforest. People were cutting down thousands of trees to make space. They wanted space to build farms or make way for big roads through the forest.

Chico Mendes and his friends knew that without the trees they would not be able to live and work. So they tried to stop people cutting down the trees.

Many people in the world agreed with Chico Mendes. But others thought he was a trouble-maker. One day, just before Christmas in 1988, Chico opened the back door of his house and somebody shot him dead. People from all over the world went to his funeral on Christmas Day, 1988.

WHAT ARE RAINFORESTS?

● Read this information about them.
Rainforests are millions of years old. They are hot and wet places. The thick tops of the trees protect the earth from the heavy rain. The spongy roots collect the rainwater and

release it slowly. When the trees are cut down, the earth is not protected and the soil is washed away. There are no roots to collect the rainwater, so there are floods and nothing can grow.

Many different kinds of plants and animals live in the rainforest. Some of them can only live in the special environment of the forest. Rainforests are important to the whole world because the trees help to take harmful carbon dioxide gas out of the air.

Many trees in the rainforest are useful to people.

- Brazil nuts come from one of the tallest trees in the forest.
- Oil for both cooking and heating comes from the nuts of a palm tree.
- Sacks are made from the trunk of the jute tree.
- Fishing nets and ropes are made from the leaves of another palm tree.
- Buttons are made from palm nuts.

People who live in the rainforest use these things themselves and make money by selling them.

RUBBER AND RUBBER-TAPPERS

The rubber tree grows in Brazil. Rubber is strong and waterproof. The people in the rainforest use rubber for making bags and shoes. We also use rubber to make hospital equipment, waterproof clothes and car tyres.

The rubber-tappers collect the rubber from the trees. Early in the morning they make a cut in the trunk of the tree and leave a cup to catch the rubber. This is called tapping. Later in the day they go back to the trees to collect the full cups.

● Now, using different coloured highlighter pens for each one, highlight all the information which tells you:

• Why Chico Mendes wanted to save the rainforests.

• Why rainforests are important to people.

• Why they are important to animals and plants.

● Now use the information which you have highlighted to fill in this report.

Why Chico Mendes? _____

One important thing about Chico Mendes is

_____

Another important thing is _____

Chico Mendes wanted to save rainforests because

_____

Rainforests are important to people because

_____

Trees are important to animals and plants because

_____

Why Chico Mendes?

Why did John Burningham dedicate this book to Chico Mendes? Here are some ideas.

● Highlight the ones you agree with most and add some ideas of your own.

He thought Chico Mendes was a brave man.

He agreed with Chico Mendes that the rainforest should be saved.

He wanted us to find out about Chico Mendes.

He wanted Chico Mendes to be remembered.

Chico Mendes gave him the idea for writing this book.

_____

_____

_____

What do you think now?

Has reading about Chico Mendes changed your mind about the most important parts of the book?

● Write what you think about the book.

When I first read the book I thought it was mostly about

_____

Now I think it is mostly about

_____

Secondly, it is about

_____

I have/haven't changed my mind because

_____

_____

I think other people should read this book because

_____

_____

If I met John Burningham I would ask him

_____

MANAGING THE READING OF *OI! GET OFF OUR TRAIN*

The activities in 'Making sense' focus on particular sequences in the book. Children's reading of the book is divided into:
• the departure of the train;
• the arrival of the elephant;
• the arrival of the crane;
• the arrival of the polar bear;
• the final four pages.

CLASSROOM MANAGEMENT AND SUPPORT

The activities will work most successfully if you have at least six copies of the book available, as some of the tasks involve close reading and reference to the book to check and refine understanding – these are flagged with the book icon.

The activities allow for a range of different groupings:
• individual (p 12–13, 16–17, 18–19);
• pairs (p 6–7, 10, 20–21);
• groups of 3/4 (p 14–15, 26);
• whole class (p 4–5).

The activity pages are addressed directly to the children, but it is recommended that you introduce the book to the whole class, to support understanding and to reinforce joint involvement in follow-on activities.

Individual writing tasks should be carried out after group or class discussion. Sometimes individual work has been suggested so that you can assess individual children's achievements.

Many activities assume children to be working with a partner. Sharing and discussing responses are important elements in helping children to develop and refine their ideas. Coming together to share outcomes also helps to reinforce learning.

DIFFERENTIATION

The activities on pages 12–13, 16–17 are suitable for children who are not yet reading fluently, perhaps because they are new to English, as they encourage revisiting the book and help children to consolidate understanding by ordering and matching words and phrases. Initial discussion will also help less fluent readers to complete these tasks.

More challenging activities are on pages 6–7, 14–15 and 24. These ask children to support their opinions using evidence from the book. Pages 20–21 provide a research task; children may need help in selecting information from appropriate sources. Pages 22–23 give another opportunity to practise reading for information skills.

Writing activities on pages 18, 19, 20–21 have a structured frame to support children's writing. Children who can handle the structures confidently can move on to independent writing as suggested in extension activities in the Teachers' notes.

TIME-SCALE

If used as a core book for English work, plan to spend two to three weeks on it, devoting three hours per week to reading and main activities. This should give time for some children to revisit activities whilst others tackle extension work.

MATCHING THE BOOK TO YOUR CLASS

Oi! Get Off Our Train raises pertinent issues about the environment in an entertaining and accessible way. It allows children to consider the choices which John Burningham made when deciding on the format of this book. Its repetitive structure uses natural language patterns which do not become stilted or rigid, and invite re-reading. The pictures are highly sophisticated and exemplify a range of art techniques.

John Burningham will almost certainly be known to the children: this could be a problem. They may need to be persuaded of the suitability of the book if they associate John Burningham with writing for young children. Try comparing the language and pictures in one of his less sophisticated books with *Oi! Get Off Our Train* to emphasise the difference.

This book is suitable for use with children who are not yet fluent readers. The repetitive structure supports reading whilst widening understanding of language patterns and vocabulary in a context which makes sense. This enables children to readily engage with its concepts and issues, which are far from 'babyish'.

TEACHING POTENTIAL

Oi! Get Off Our Train offers learning opportunities in the following curriculum areas:

English
• making detailed study of a book by a well-known author;
• responding imaginatively to a text;
• evaluating reading;
• supporting opinions with reference to text;

• using information texts to identify and select information;
• presenting findings;
• questioning and clarifying personal opinions and those of others;
• engaging in different kinds of writing – narrative, dialogue, argument.

Geography and Science
• environmental change – local and global;
• weather.

SPECIAL TERMINOLOGY

It would be helpful if children know the following vocabulary:
• draft;
• character;
• rainforest;
• endangered species;
• environment;
• dedication;
• author/illustrator.

BACKGROUND KNOWLEDGE

Children will need to be familiar with the idea of returning to a book several times to explore different aspects of it. It would also be helpful if they have undertaken some preliminary work on writing speech and writing narrative and if they can recognise the difference between the two. They will also need to have used information books in order to select particular information.

RESOURCES

You will need a globe in order to locate Brazil and the rainforest. Provide a selection of information books on the environment, animals in general and endangered species in particular, as well as pictures or posters of the rainforest environment.

Books by John Burningham (all published by Red Fox unless otherwise stated):
Borka : The Adventures of a Goose with No Feathers
Trubloff
Cannonball Simp
Come Away from the Water, Shirley
Time to Get Out of the Bath, Shirley
Would you Rather ...
The Shopping Basket
Avocado Baby
Where's Julius?
John Patrick Norman McHennessy
Courtney
Aldo
The Baby; The Blanket; The Dog; The Friend; The Snow; The Rabbit; The Cupboard; The School (Red Fox Little Books)
Granpa (Picture Puffin)
Harvey Slumfenburger's Christmas Present (Walker Books)
Mr Gumpy's Outing (Picture Puffin)
Mr Gumpy's Motor Car (Picture Puffin)

Books with an environmental theme
Tigress, Helen Cowcher (Andre Deutsch)
Antarctica, Helen Cowcher (Andre Deutsch)
The World that Jack Built, Ruth Brown (Red Fox)
Dinosaurs and All That Rubbish, Michael Foreman (Penguin)
One World, Michael Foreman (Red Fox)
The Whales' Song, Dyan Sheldon and Gary Blythe (Red Fox)

Books about change over time
Window, Jeannie Baker (Red Fox)
Where the Forest Meets the Sea, Jeannie Baker (Walker)
Katie Morag and the New Pier, Mairi Hedderwick (Red Fox)

Books with a cumulative structure
Bringing the Rain to Kapiti Plain, Verna Aardema (Macmillan Children's Books)
Honey Hunters, Francesca Martin (Walker Books)

The Shopping Basket, John Burningham (Red Fox)
On the Way Home, Jill Murphy (Macmillan Children's Books)
Tick Tock, Eileen Browne (Walker Books)
Eat up Gemma, Sarah Hayes (Walker Books)

Non-fiction and poetry
Earthways, Earthwise: Poems on Conservation, ed Judith Nicholls (OUP)

Useful addresses
World Wide Fund for Nature
Weyside Park
Godalming
Surrey GU7 1XR

Friends of the Earth
(Youth Action Earth Action)
26–28 Underwood Street
London N1 7QJ

Greenpeace
30–31 Islington Green
London N1 8XE

Watch
The Green
Witham Park
Lincoln LN5 7JR

Woodcraft Folk
13 Ritherden Road
London SW17 8QE

Young Ornithologists' Club
The Lodge
Sandy
Bedfordshire SG19 2DL

Young People's Trust for Endangered Species
95 Woodbridge Road
Guildford
Surrey GU1 4PX

Oi! Get Off Our Train

TEACHERS' NOTES

WAYS IN
WHAT CAN WE FIND OUT FROM THE COVER?
Aim: to predict the story from information on the cover.
Teaching points: introduce the book to the whole class. Focus on title, author, and picture separately at first and then together.
Extension: compare other Burningham covers.

MAKING SENSE
IS IT A BOY OR A GIRL?
Aim: to speculate about a question, using clues from words and pictures.
Teaching points: this is an open-ended question and some children may feel strongly one way or the other. Ensure they find evidence to support their point of view. There may be a gender difference in opinion, so start with single sex groups and then let a pair of girls join with a pair of boys to discuss responses. Alternatively, if children feel secure with each other, a mixed boy/girl pairing may lead to lively debate!
Extension: consider whether Burningham deliberately left it open ended. Why? Does it matter whether it is a boy or a girl?

THE ELEPHANT
Aim: to infer what characters are thinking, based on knowledge of the story.
Teaching points: children need to think about what the characters are thinking and how they will express these thoughts. Model examples from books/comics if they are inexperienced with speech bubble writing. Explain that they should give their own opinion, not try to find the 'right' answer. A whole class discussion would be useful either before or after individual work.
Extension: repeat the activity with other pages and characters in the book.

THE CRANE
Aims: to use the repetitive structure to recap on the story so far and to predict the next episode.
Teaching points: children should complete the chart from memory if possible but allow reference to the book if requested. Encourage imaginative predictions of the next events, based on their knowledge of the story so far.
Extension: use the chart as an on-going reading log. Completed charts are an at-a-glance summary of the repetitive narrative part of the book.

... AND SOON THERE WILL BE NONE OF US LEFT
Aim: to represent information.
Teaching points: this activity supports reading for children for whom English is an additional language. The mapping activity supports the writing. Children may need to refer back to the book for help with the mapping. Encourage them to write about the animals using their own words not simply copying from the text.
Extension: use information books to find out more about other endangered animals.

WAS IT ALL A DREAM?
Aim: to reflect on the whole book in the light of the ending.
Teaching points: children may find extra clues in the book. This is an opportunity to consider how opinions change as books are read. Groups or whole class can share their different impressions at various points during the reading of the book.
Extension: children can consider what the author's view is. Is the last page a red herring or an invitation to reconsider the whole book? Does it invite us to re-read the book?

Oi! Get Off Our Train

DEVELOPING IDEAS
THE WEATHER

Aim: to consolidate understanding of the story by focusing on a specific aspect.

Teaching points: ordering and matching text reinforces reading and is of particular benefit to non-fluent readers or to bilingual children who are fairly new to English. The children can refer to the book for support. Individual responses will enable you to assess understanding.

Extension: input the information into a computer and the children can learn or practise moving text around on screen. They can re-order the vocabulary, entered in a random list, using cut and paste commands. Children can choose other pages and write speech bubbles for other characters.

THE PYJAMA-CASE DOG'S TRAIN JOURNEY

Aim: to write an account from a particular point of view.

Teaching points: the writing frame supports children by asking them to select information and to write an appropriate amount in each section.

Extension: children who use the writing frame confidently can write an unsupported account of the pyjama-case dog's journey. Compile the children's work into an illustrated book for younger children.

TOO MANY ANIMALS

Aim: to write arguments in dialogue form, based on a situation in the book.

Teaching points: initial class or group discussion to brainstorm ideas would be helpful for some children. Give all children the opportunity to think and write both sides of the argument, thinking of counter arguments for each point as it arises. Encourage pairs to role-play and improvise the dialogue, and bring in more children for the second part of the activity.

Extension: children can write a scripted version of the conversation and work it up into a short scene for two–four voices, with sound effects, music and/or brief staging notes. Simple props or masks would make this an unusual presentation piece for another class or group, or for assembly.

ENDANGERED SPECIES

Aim: to use the book as a trigger for research and a model for independent writing.

Teaching points: have available animal information books. It is also possible to do the activity with storybook presentations about different animals. Encourage children to imitate Burningham's format and style. Provide a simple sentence starter: 'Please let me come …' for less confident children who can then find two or three points for their chosen animal. Pairs of children can decide collaboratively which animal to choose and what information to include, and share the writing and drawing tasks if appropriate.

Extension: use completed pages as first drafts for full-size pages with finished artwork. Ask children to swap and suggest improvements for each others' work. Encourage them to adopt some of the art techniques and styles shown in the book – collage, water-colour, crayon and so on. The children will need to sequence the new pages, and could then assemble them into a book to present to younger classes or at school assembly.

WHO WAS CHICO MENDES?

Aim: to look at dedications and explore links between stories and factual writing.

Teaching points: model examples of dedications in other books (Burningham books often have them). Explain that they are often very personal, but that not all books have one. Indicate Brazil and the extent of the rainforest around the Amazon river on a globe. This is a simple information-retrieval activity but if necessary, model the highlighting and the note-taking tasks before they attempt it individually or in pairs. Space is restricted to prevent children merely copying chunks of text. This leads into the next activity 'Why Chico Mendes?' and children may begin to think about the connection for themselves.

Extension: able children can consider the differences in the language of the story (repetitive, like spoken language) and the information writing (more formal, impersonal). Why is the Chico Mendes information more difficult to read?

WHY CHICO MENDES?

Aims: to consider one theme of the book in the light of new information.

Teaching points: interestingly, Chico Mendes was not so much concerned with saving the environment of the rainforest for the animals and plants as to save the livelihoods of the rubber-tappers. Burningham's book is however about endangered animals, with no overt political agenda, except for the dedication. They should speculate and re-evaluate their reading of the book in the light of what they have learned about the dedication.

Extension: children can research dedications in other books and think about why the writers included them. They can reach some general conclusions about what dedications are for and why an author might write one.

EVALUATION
WHAT DO YOU THINK NOW?

Aim: to re-evaluate the book in the light of additional evidence.

Teaching points: active readers will change their opinion of a book as they read it and this is an important part of the reading process.

Extension: children can read other Burningham books and research his writing biography. Show them how to look at copyright lines to find out the date of first publication and then produce a timeline of his publishing. Illustrate with book covers or illustrations from the books. Children can compare two different Burningham titles, looking at the illustration style and the language to see how his style has evolved over time.

Oi! Get Off Our Train